DING DONG BELL

A First Book of Nursery Rhymes

Devised by
PERCY YOUNG
and
EDWARD ARDIZZONE

DOVER PUBLICATIONS, INC.
NEW YORK

This Dover edition, first published in 1969, is an
unabridged and unaltered republication of the work
originally published in 1957. This edition is published by special arrangement with Dobson Books,
Ltd., London, publishers of the original edition.

Standard Book Number: 486-21248-3
Library of Congress Catalog Card Number: 69-17097

Manufactured in the United States of America
Dover Publications, Inc.
180 Varick Street
New York, N. Y. 10014

CONTENTS

MRS MORRINGTON: I must show you a new book I have bought you, and then I will
   go in and take off my bonnet.
ALL: Oh! Let us see it. *(Mrs M. gives it to them)*
HENRIETTA: Have you read it, Mother?
MRS MORRINGTON: Yes, I read it this morning in the steamboat. I hope you will in
   future be at no loss for amusements in your play-hours.

. . . .

JULIET:... as I have not yet begun to learn music, I do not think that ugly tunes are
   pretty.
MRS MORRINGTON: *(Smiling)* Explain yourself.

Miss Leslie's *Occupation for Play Hours*
(Boston, Mass., 1831)

...... calculated to amuse Children and to excite them to sleep.

Mother Goose's Melody, or Sonnets for the Cradle (1791)

PREFACE

Tell tale twit [1]
Your tongue will split
And all the little dogs
Will have a little bit!

FOR A FEW YEARS now these lines have been opprobriously used by an indignant brother to an equally indignant sister—and *vice versa*. One day I took the small girl aside and pointed to what might reasonably be accepted as an authentic version:

Tell tale tit
Your tongue shall be slit
And all the dogs in our town
Shall have a bit.

So it was inscribed in *Mother Goose's Melody*. 'Stupid!' said the girl, oblivious of any academic nicety, 'that book's wrong'. She was, of course, right; for folk art is an evolving art, and when it can be contemplated in a 'definitive' version it can only be dead.

As it happens the nursery rhyme (with its music) is virtually the only surviving art of the people in the western world. Therefore it is important from time to time to emphasise its living quality.

It is an open question whether the words or the music are of greater significance. It is, however, indisputable that each element constitutes the beginning of poetic and musical experience for all of us. In the past the fact has been recognised insofar as music and, to a lesser degree, words have been accommodated to the imaginative climate of a particular period. From the seventeenth to the nineteenth century tunes were arranged within the general musical idiom of the day, while words slipped in and out of broadsheets, chapbooks, and other collections according to their current usage. In the nineteenth century standards of propriety were so high that many words, familiar in most nursery conversation, were banned; presumably for fear of the possible contamination of adult morality. In the present edition, and on the advice of available babes and sucklings, some stronger meat has been withdrawn from refrigeration.

As will be noticed in many instances in this book a large number of nursery rhymes were once popular ballads which winged their way from tavern to tavern, from fair to fair. Children inevitably picked them up, and sensibly edited them after the pattern

---

[1] Quoted by permission of M.E.Y. In line 3 'birds' may be substituted for 'dogs' *ad lib.*

of their own imagination. In the process nonsense was generally shown to be more sensible than sense.

Some historical information is included in the notes on the songs; but it is to be hoped that no one who uses the book will think such details of prime importance. The archaeologist, the anthropologist, the psychologist, and so on, have all had a fairly long innings in this field—with the result that the fun of the game has almost been squeezed out. That this has not entirely happened is due, so far as we see it, to the creative and recreative talents of the children who are the custodians of this part of our heritage.

This, then, is no academic book, and the versions of the words are simply those that we like. Sometimes the form in which they appear is that presented by our children; sometimes an old and vigorous form is preferred; sometimes a mixture of old and new—especially where there may have been difficulties in scanning the words to the tunes. And sometimes verses which have dropped out of successive editions have been restored, either to make better narrative or more varied poetry.

In the long run the poetry of nursery rhymes has suffered rather less than the music from the improving hand of the well-intentioned. For some long time certain conditions have been observed in the arrangement of children's music. It should be easy to play—for the adult that is; it should contain no noises unacceptable to the conventional ear. Compulsory education has virtually made these conditions obligatory. The result is that by an undue regard for the indolent imagination of the adult who plays nursery rhymes because he or — more likely — she must, children are being depressed by musical standards only apt to an academy for adult beginners in the theory of music.

The persuasive pen of the artist can work as it will in illustrating nursery rhymes. I have allowed myself the same luxury in setting the music. It is often frankly illustrative music, derived from a reasonably up-to-date vocabulary. Up-to-date to this extent: that children find some of the noises not dissimilar to those that they sometimes discover and appreciate at the keyboard, and adults, brought up to the formal run of harmony-to-the-dominant-seventh, slightly alarming. I am encouraged, however, that Elizabeth, *aetat.* 2, sat the whole book through as they were played to her one evening. Thus it was felt that in some respects it lived up to the motto from *Mother Goose's Melody* which faces the Preface.

These pieces may be played to children, used as accompaniments to their singing or played by children. No directions regarding speed are given, for the right *tempo* depends on an appreciation of the words and varying standards of keyboard technique. In short the performer must use his own judgement and imagination. Some few hints are included, however, to aid performance and musical understanding. Any terms with a technical flavour — with such words children delight in spicing their stock of knowledge — are clearly shown; and there are just enough of them to serve the young musician until he is old enough to pass on to some other, more ambitious book.

There are those who feel a purist's urge to sing traditional tunes without accompaniment. They are welcome to dispense with these accompaniments so long as they look at some of the songs which have been rescued from desuetude. But the youngster who eagerly anticipates each Saturday morning for his weekly feast of *Children's Choice*, scooped up by Uncle this or Auntie that, will prefer less purism and more punch.

In devising this collection we set out to enjoy ourselves, but also to see the subject from the vantage point of the modern or — should we say — the eternal child. So we may excuse our pieces in the words of Ann and Jane Taylor — 'In the *Nursery* they are designed to circulate; and within its sanctuary walls, the writer and artist claim shelter from the eye of criticism: though, should they appear to have admitted any *sentiment*, injudicious, erroneous, or dangerous, they ask not such an indulgence.'

P.M.Y.

For Elizabeth and James

1 Pussy's in the Well

Some things are easier to describe musically than others. Bells for instance. So here the ding and the dong are to be heard nearly all the time. When you have got used to ding and dong try to think of them as doh and soh, two sounds which play an important part in all music. This you will see in a good many places elsewhere in this book.

The only mark of expression is mf (mezzo-forte = fairly loud). Beyond this add your own expression as the words seem to want it. This applies throughout the book.

2 Little Pussy

I love lit - tle puss - y, Her coat is so warm: And if I don't hurt her, She'll do me no harm.

(2) So I'll not pull her tail,
    Or drive her away;
    But Pussy and I
    Together will play.

(3) She will sit by my side,
    And I'll give her food;
    And she'll like me because
    I am gentle and good.

This is a happier picture of a cat than the last—a comfortable fireside scene. In the bass there is only one note (E flat = doh). This is called a pedal *note, and is often used by composers when it is desired to suggest something tranquil, peaceful, sleepy... Can you make up a 'sleepy' tune at the keyboard and hold down* doh *in the left hand? Try.*

3 Pussy Cat, Pussy Cat

Melodies of nursery rhymes are generally very simple in design. Here we have a four bar sentence, which is repeated. One note, however, is different the second time. Which is it? There are some staccato marks in the next to the last bar. Make the notes as short as you can so that the music sounds a little frightened.

4 *Hickory, Dickory, Dock!*

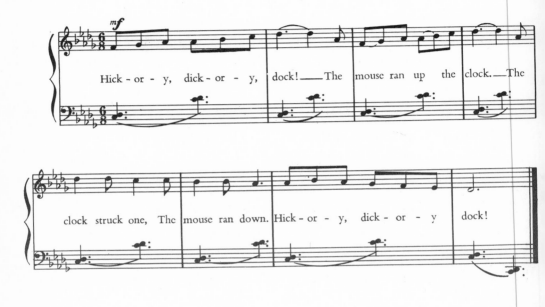

Hick - or - y, dick - or - y, dock! — The mouse ran up the clock. — The clock struck one, The mouse ran down. Hick - or - y, dick - or - y dock!

This is a story of high doh *and low* doh *— up and down the clock by scale passages. The left hand part makes the kind of noise that my clock makes. If yours is different try to find some other notes on the piano that will suit, and then put them where mine are in the left hand.*

5 *There Was a Pig*

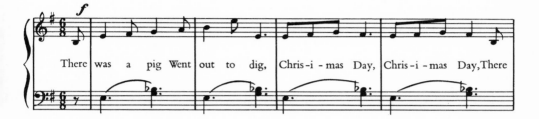

There was a pig Went out to dig, Chris-i-mas Day, Chris-i-mas Day, There

was a pig Went out to dig, On Chris-i-mas Day in t' morn-ing.

(2) There was a cow
Went out to plough,
Chrisimas Day, etc.

(3) There was a sparrow
Went out to harrow,
Chrisimas Day, etc.

(4) There was a drake
Went out to rake,
Chrisimas Day, etc.

(5) There was a crow
Went out to sow,
Chrisimas Day, etc.

(6) There was a sheep
Went out to reap,
Chrisimas Day, etc.

(7) There was a minnow
Went out to winnow,
Chrisimas Day, etc.

6 Baa, Baa, Black Sheep

Here are four beautifully balanced, and contrasted phrases; each of four bars. Notice, however, how closely related are the last three phrases. Each is based on a downward scale passage.

Play the first eight bars of the left hand part. Now play the last eight bars. These phrases are exactly the same, except that the second is an upside-down version of the first!

7 Oh Where, Oh Where is My Little Dog Gone?

We generally find that dogs have a sense of humour. I am sure that the dog that I used to have would have liked the comic way in which the accompaniment of this waltz tune behaves. Every now and then you may have to count to get the left hand rhythm quite right. But so long as no one hears you that doesn't matter.

8 There Was a Little Dog

There was a lit - tle dog sit - ting by the fire - side; Out

popped a lit - tle coal, And in the lit - tle dog - gie's tail it

burnt a lit - tle hole. A - way ran the lit - tle dog, to

seek a lit - tle pool To cool his lit - tle tail, And for

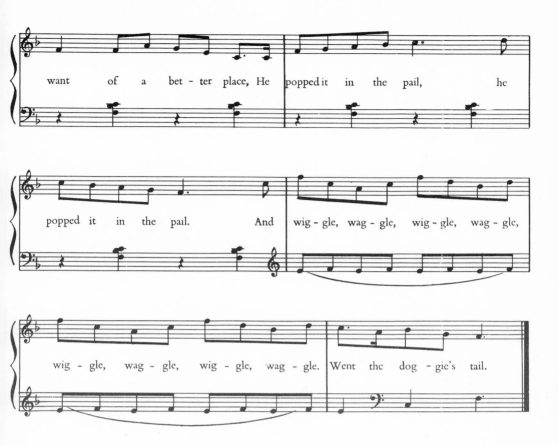

want of a bet - ter place, He popped it in the pail, he

popped it in the pail. And wig - gle, wag - gle, wig - gle, wag - gle,

wig - gle, wag - gle, wig - gle, wag - gle. Went the dog - gie's tail.

A boy who knows something about music walked in when I was finishing playing the piece, and asked whether it was anything to do with a piece by Handel called 'The Arrival of the Queen of Sheba' (well known through its arrangement for piano, or two pianos). I said it hadn't, but it might have. For, like many other nursery tunes, it has a flavour of the eighteenth century —the age of Handel. You may feel this especially in the last three bars, where the melody notes form arpeggios.

9 Kittens and Mittens

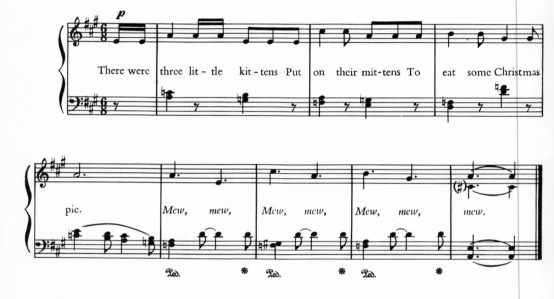

There were three lit-tle kit-tens Put on their mit-tens To eat some Christmas pie.

Mew, mew, Mew, mew, Mew, mew, mew.

(2) These three little kittens
   They lost their mittens,
   And all began to cry.
   Mew, mew, etc.

(3) 'Go, go, naughty kittens,
   And find your mittens,
   Or you shan't have any pie.'
   Mew, mew, etc.

(4) These three little kittens
   They found their mittens,
   And joyfully they did cry.
   Mew, mew, etc.

(5) 'Oh, Granny, dear!
    Our mittens are here,
    Make haste and cut up the pie!'
    Purr—rr, purr—rr, purr—rr.

Another study in soh *and* doh, *but with 'me' also playing an important part in the out-line of the melody. These kittens are, at first at any rate, sad. That is why the first chord is a minor chord, in spite of the fact that the melody itself is in a major key.*

10 Three Blind Mice

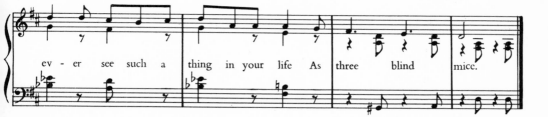

ev - er see such a thing in your life As three blind mice.

As you probably know you can make a canon or round out of this. To do so you need two singers. The second (who must be an independent sort of person) will start when the first has reached the beginning of the fifth bar. If you (and your friend) are ambitious enough to produce a canon you must leave out the accompaniment. Unaccompanied singing (which is called a cappella by those who know a lot about musical terms) is sometimes thought to be a bit highbrow. But don't worry about that. When Thomas Ravenscroft wrote this tune down, more than three hundred years ago, there weren't any highbrows. Or if there were everybody was one.

11 The Bat

Compare with 'The Star' on p. 132. The words, by Lewis Carroll, are a parody. And so is the music, which comes from a collection called Birds and Beasts *(pub. E. J. Arnold). Notice how as in 'There Was a Pig' the familiar tune is turned into a minor key. And what a difference this makes to its character.*

BIRDS & INSECTS

12 *The Goose and the Gander*

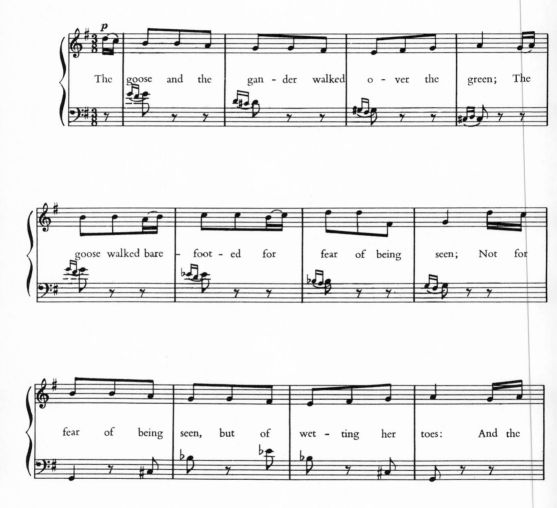

The goose and the gan - der walked o - ver the green; The goose walked bare - foot - ed for fear of being seen; Not for fear of being seen, but of wet - ting her toes: And the

man that drinks   strong beer hath a   jol - ly red   nose.

(2) The blacksmith is black, but his silver is white,
And he sits in the alehouse from morning till night.
Tang dillo, tang dillo, tang dillo, tang dillo,
And happy is the man that sits under the willow.

I am not sure what this is all about, but it is an entertaining mixture of half-remembered ideas; a kind of dream. The accompaniment to the melody (an eight bar phrase exactly repeated) borrows its ideas from the words. Thus a number of unexpected notes jostle one against the other.

13 Goosey, Goosey Gander

It is the first group of four quavers which sets the melody going. So this group thoroughly infects the left hand part, where 'goosey, goosey gander' turns up four times — twice the wrong way up. You may (probably will) want to practise the last bar, otherwise the old man will fall down too many, or too few, stairs.

14 *Bye, Birdie*

Bye, bird - ie, in a bo - gie, In a - mang a pic - kle fog-gie.

But the bird - ie was a - wa', And we sought it man-y a day.

Till we found it out at last, Drai - gled in a wild duck's nest.

The words of this song cannot easily be put into English and should be appreciated for their poetic sounds. From the many meanings of the difficult words these are the most appropriate: bogie, *dream;* pickle foggie, *small mossy place;* draigled, *covered with mud. Notice how economical is the melody with its range of only five notes.*

15 *Little Cock Sparrow*

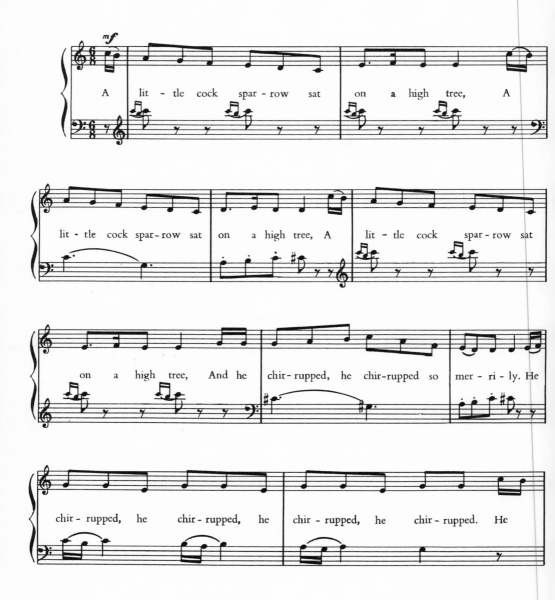

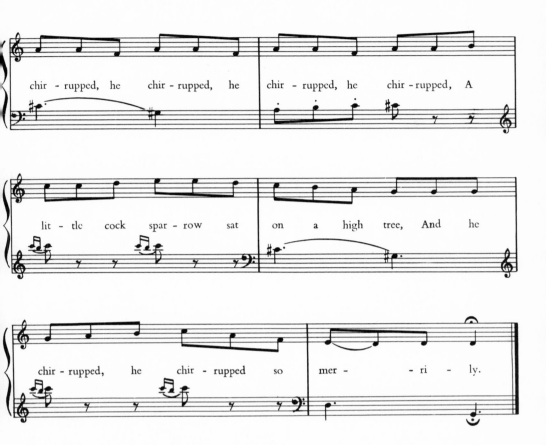

chir - rupped, he   chir - rupped, he   chir - rupped, he   chir - rupped, A

lit - tle   cock   spar - row   sat   on   a   high   tree,   And   he

chir - rupped,   he   chir - rupped   so   mer -   - ri - ly.

(2) A naughty little boy with a bow and arrow,
   Determined to shoot this little cock sparrow;

(3) For this little cock sparrow would make a nice stew,
   And his giblets would make a nice little pie too.

(4) 'Oh no', says cock sparrow, 'I won't make a stew',
   And he fluttered his wings, and away he flew.

This was first printed in Walter Crane's Baby's Bouquet, *and seems to have been missed by everyone since. It is a charming tune—with a genuine bird-call in the middle—and a little unexpected. You will see that it ends on ray instead of doh. It doesn't, therefore, seem to finish quite firmly. But then we can think that the little cock sparrow never stops singing. To play this effectively you will have to learn to cross your left hand over your right—then you will find the bird at the top of the tree.*

16 *Carrion Crow*

A car-rion crow sat on an oak, *Derr-y derr-y, derr-y, dec - co;* A car - rion crow sat on an oak, Watch-ing a tai - lor shap-ing his cloak. *Heigh - ho! the car - rion crow, Derr-y derr-y derr-y, dec - co*

(2) 'Oh wife, bring me my old bent bow',
Derry, derry, derry, decco;
'Oh wife, bring me my old bent bow,
That I may shoot yon carrion crow.'
Heigh-ho! the carrion crow,
Derry, derry, derry, decco.

(3) The tailor shot, and he missed his mark,
    Derry, derry, derry, decco;
    The tailor shot, and he missed his mark,
    And he shot his old sow right through the heart.
    Heigh-ho! the carrion crow,
    Derry, derry, derry, decco.

(4) 'Oh wife, bring brandy in a spoon',
    Derry, derry, derry, decco.
    'Oh wife, bring brandy in a spoon,
    For our old sow is in a swoon.'
    Heigh-ho! the carrion crow,
    Derry, derry, derry, decco.

What fun! This melody 'goes in canon'. See also 'Three Blind Mice'.

17 *Birds are Singing*

Birds are sing-ing, Pleas-ure bring-ing, Earth a-gain with smiles to cheer;

Glad we meet you, Glad we greet you, O ye signs of spring-time dear.

(2) Winter's sadness,
 Notes of gladness.
 Sung by you drive far away;
 Sweetly swelling,
 Care dispelling,
 Let your music longer stay.

(3) He who made you,
 Kindly bade you
 Live to cheer our life with song;
 While we ever
 Thank the giver,
 Dear shall be your lovely throng.

*This is taken from a Victorian collection—*Fifty Songs for Young People, *arranged and partly composed by Charles Henry Purday. The picture on the cover shows a happy family group of a hundred years ago, and both words and melody recall those days.*

18 Poor Robin

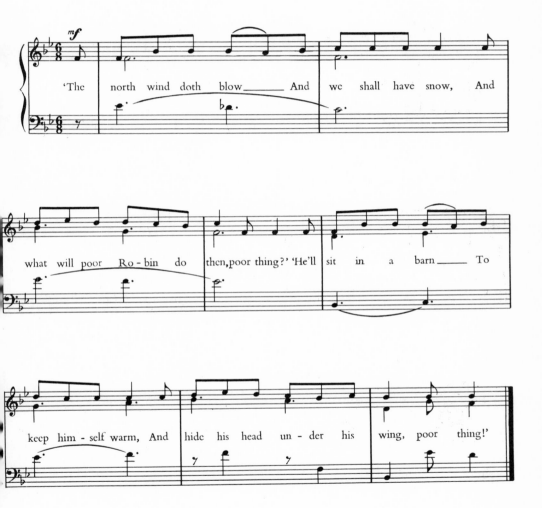

'The north wind doth blow___ And we shall have snow, And what will poor Ro-bin do then, poor thing?' 'He'll sit in a barn___ To keep him-self warm, And hide his head un-der his wing, poor thing!'

Another melody in which the second phrase is a slender variation of the first. In bar 2 there is an unexpected D flat in the left hand—to give the effect of the cold. In the next to the last bar the bass part—notice the rests—hides the robin's head.

19 *Little Busy Bee*

How doth the lit-tle bu-sy bee Im-prove each shin-ing hour: And

ga-ther ho-ney all the day From e-v'ry o-p'n-ing flow'r. 2. How

skil-ful-ly she builds her cells, How neat she spreads her wax, And

la - bours hard to store it well, With the sweet food she makes.

(3) In works of labour, and of skill,
     I would be busy too;
     For Satan finds some mischief still,
     For idle hands to do.

(4) In books, or work, or healthful play
     Let my first years be past;
     That I may give for every day
     Some good account at last.

Isaac Watts published his Divine Songs for Children *in 1715. He was a pioneer in the writing of poetry for children and therefore deserves our gratitude. He believed that children could be taught as well as entertained by poetry. So this tale of the bee is an encouragement to work hard! The melody is from* Fifty Songs for Young People. *You can improve the shining hour by practising demi-semiquavers in the left hand; they make the bee buzz.*

20 Miss Muffet and the Spider

Spiders are among the creepie-crawlies. So that explains why part of a chromatic scale is to be heard in the left hand from the fifth bar onwards. This setting does not come to a full stop; the music, like Miss Muffet, is frightened away. And that is how it should seem when you play it.

FLOWERS & TREES

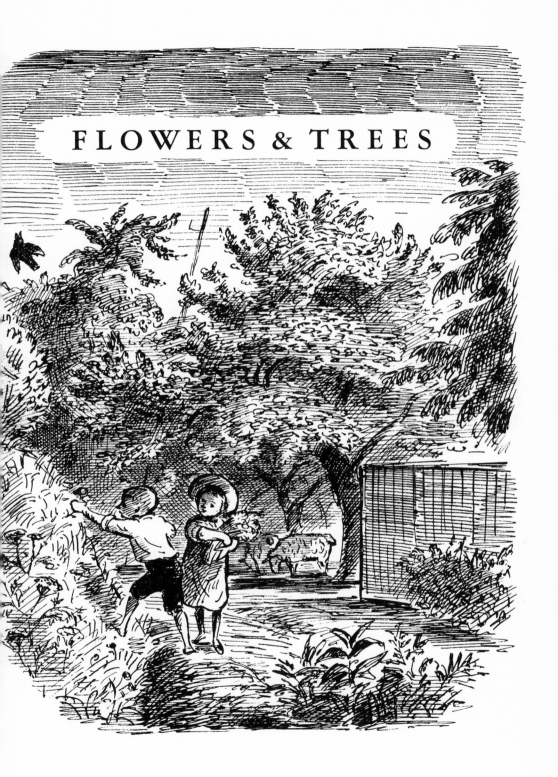

21 Round the Mulberry Bush

Here we go round the mul-berry bush, the mul-berry bush, the mul-berry bush;

Here we go round the mul-berry bush, All on a frost-y morn-ing.

This is the way we clap our hands, This is the way we clap our hands,

This is   the   way   we   clap   our hands, All   on   a   frost - y   morn - ing.

'*This is the way we . . . .*': *You may go on inventing actions for as long as you like.*
This is another singing-game—a round dance. You will discover that this rhythm—in 6/8 time—
makes you want to dance, or skip. This usually happens with quick pieces in this rhythm.

You will often read that music is 'international'. This tune helps one to believe that. We
think of it as a good old English tune. In fact it wandered out of England and into France during
the eighteenth century where it became naturalised.

This tune became widely popular when it was introduced into an opera—Love in a Village—
in 1762. Nowadays it is the cinema which often popularises a melody.

45

22 *Rosy Apple*

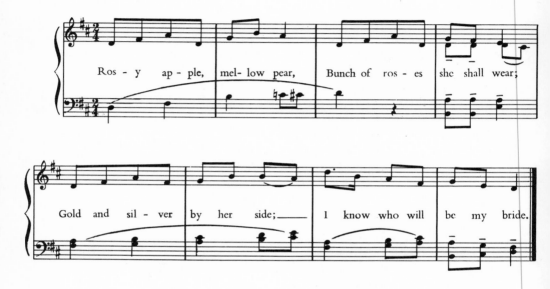

Ros - y ap - ple, mel- low pear, Bunch of ros - es she shall wear;

Gold and sil - ver by her side;_____ I know who will be my bride.

(2) Take her by the lily-white hand,
    Lead her 'cross the water,
    Give her kisses, one, two, three,
    (Mrs. Harrison's) daughter

This is an enchanting singing-game from Derbyshire. The tune is almost sedate (music in 2/4 time always seems to have something of this quality behind its gaiety). Notice how the first bar of melody is repeated at intervals. In the words of the second verse you can put anybody in place of Mrs Harrison, depending on whose daughter you happen to know best.

23 *Lavender's Blue*

Lav - en - der's blue, did - dle, did - dle, Lav - en - der's green,

When I am King, did - dle, did - dle, You shall be Queen.

(2) Call up your men, diddle, diddle!
    Set them to work;
    Some to the plough, diddle, diddle!
    Some to the cart.

(3) Some to make hay, diddle, diddle!
    Some to cut corn;
    While you and I, diddle, diddle!
    Keep ourselves warm.

I always think of this as a song which 'shines'. See how bright the words are, or their vowel sounds, and how the mid-way resting place lies on the highest note of the melody. To make the music sound bright it is set an octavo higher than you would sing it.

24 *I Had a Little Nut Tree*

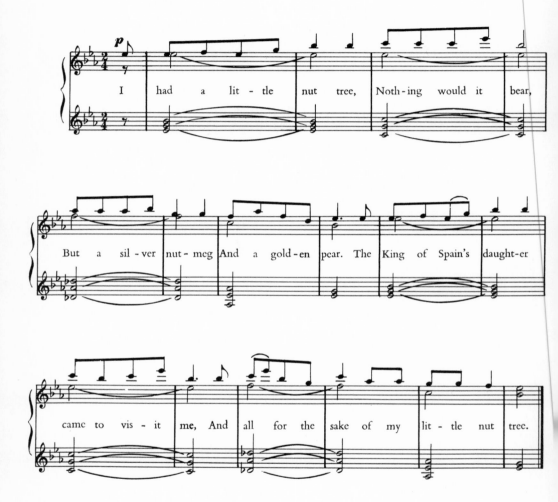

I had a lit - tle nut tree, Noth-ing would it bear,

But a sil - ver nut - meg And a gold - en pear. The King of Spain's daught-er

came to vis - it me, And all for the sake of my lit - tle nut tree.

This also is set in a higher octave. The 'silver nutmeg' suggested this. The *King of Spain's daughter* is thought to have been the Princess Joanna of Castille, who came to England in the early years of the sixteenth century. Many nursery rhymes have their origin in some historical event—but mostly they show a good deal more of poetry than of history.

25 *Ring-a-Ring o' Roses*

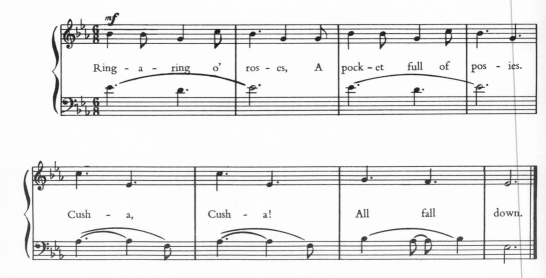

Ring - a - ring o' ros - es, A pock - et full of pos - ies.
Cush - a, Cush - a! All fall down.

Another singing-game in 6/8 time. When you are playing this, or similar pieces, don't be so anxious about getting the 'right rhythm' that you put a heavy accent on what are sometimes called the 'strong beats' (to which in this you might count 1..2..). If you do, the music will clump along, and there will be no lightness of step. And that, of course, is what is required.

26 Nuts in May

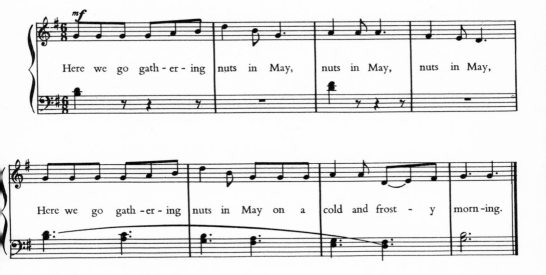

Here we go gath-er-ing nuts in May, nuts in May, nuts in May,

Here we go gath-er-ing nuts in May on a cold and frost-y morn-ing.

Compare this with 'Round the Mulberry Bush'. The same tune, more or less. The slight differences which you may note in the melody show the way in which alterations could creep in when music was handed down by oral tradition.

27 Month of Flowers

Sing the joy - ful month of flowers, Breathe the sweet air free - ly,

Hap - py who en - joy May hours, Na - ture's sweet - est gift is ours; Sing

gai - ly, sing gai - ly, sing gai - ly, Now is the month of May.

(2) Hear the spring air murmuring,
    Hear the stirring bushes;
    Songs from wood and cottage ring,
    Hear the bird, as on the wing
    He rushes, he rushes, he rushes
    Swiftly through the air.

(3) Deck with flowers your flowing hair,
    Deck with flower wreaths freely;
    Spring hath brought thee sure relief
    From all care and causeless grief.
    Sing gaily, sing gaily, sing gaily,
    Now is the month of May.

A third piece from Fifty Songs for Young People. *The rhythm of the left hand hops about towards the end. Why? Because the poet was so insistent on—'gaily, gaily, gaily...' So the feeling of the word is emphasised.*

28 *Mary's Garden*

'Mary, Mary, quite con-tra-ry, How does your gar-den grow?' 'With sil-ver bells and cock-le shells, And pret-ty maids all in a row, _____ And pret-ty maids all in a row.'

There is one touch of canon in this setting. Can you find it?

PEOPLE

29 *Children on Ice*

Three chil-dren slid-ing on the ice, Up-on a sum-mer's day, As it fell out, they all fell in, The rest they ran a - way.

(2) Now had these children been at home,
Or sliding on dry ground,
Ten thousand pounds to one penny,
They had not all been drowned.

(3) You parents all that children have,
And you that have got none,
If you would have them safe abroad,
Pray keep them safe at home.

Parody is a word which has already occurred once or twice in this book. As you will have learned it means making fun of something by imitation. And not very flattering imitation. I wonder whether you can guess what these words parody?

Look at a tune listed as in Common Metre *in any hymn book. It will, you will find, fit these words exactly. So 'Three Children sliding on the ice' started life, in the reign of Charles I, as a parody of a metrical psalm (or hymn). The melody to which the words were finally fitted was that of a popular ballad—'Chevy Chase'. Once tunes became well known they served many different sets of verses.*

30 Jack Horner

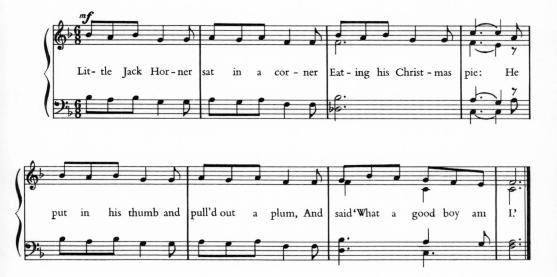

Lit-tle Jack Hor-ner sat in a cor-ner Eat-ing his Christ-mas pie: He put in his thumb and pull'd out a plum, And said 'What a good boy am I.'

A different setting of this melody may be found on p. 42. This arrangement is much more comfortable: there are no spiders in the story.

In fact there once was a Horner. (Jack here simply means a rogue, and it used to be applied to anyone of supposedly inferior rank—so 'Jacky boy' . . .) Horner was a Somerset man who did well for himself at the time of the Dissolution of the Monasteries in the reign of Henry VIII. Hence—'he pulled out a plum'.

31 *Mrs Bond*

'Oh, what have you got for din - ner, Mrs Bond?' 'There's beef in the lar- der, and ducks in the pond;' 'Dil - ly, dil - ly, dil - ly, dil - ly, come to be killed, For you must be stuffed, and my cus - to - mers filled!'

(2) 'Send us the beef first, good Mrs Bond,
And get us some ducks dressed out of the pond.'
Cry, *Dilly, dilly*, etc.

(3) 'John Ostler, go fetch me a duckling or two,'
'Ma'am', says John Ostler, 'I'll try what I can do.'
Cry, *Dilly, dilly*, etc.

(4) 'I have been to the ducks that swim in the pond,
But I found they won't come to be killed, Mrs Bond.'
I cried, *Dilly, dilly*, etc.

(5) Mrs Bond she flew down to the pond in a rage,
With plenty of onions and plenty of sage,
She cried, *Dilly, dilly*, etc.

(6) She cried, 'Little wag-tails, come and be killed,
For you must be stuffed and my customers filled!
Dilly, dilly, dilly, dilly, etc.

*At first many songs which are now nursery songs were popular among adults. This is one.
For the earliest version I have found is in a book entitled* The Thrush: A Choice Selection
of the Most Admired Popular Songs, *which was published in 1827.*

*The left hand takes a little time to warm up. When it does it amuses itself by announcing
the 'dilly, dilly' pattern before the melody.*

32 Aiken Drum

There cam a man to our town, to our town, to our town, There
cam a man to our town, and his name was Wil - lie Wood;   And he
played up - on a raz - or, a raz - or, a raz - or, And he
played up - on a raz - or, and his name was Wil - lie Wood.

(2) His hat was made o' the guid roast beef, etc.,
    And his name was Willie Wood.

(3) His coat was made of the haggis bag, etc.,
    And his name was Willie Wood.

(4) His buttons were made of the baubee baps, etc.,
    And his name was Willie Wood.

(5) But another man cam to the town, etc.,
    And they ca'd him Aiken Drum.

(6) And he played upon a ladle, etc.,
    And they ca'd him Aiken Drum.

(7) And he ate up a' the guid roast-beef, etc.,
    And his name was Aiken Drum.

(8) And he ate up a' the haggis bag, etc.,
    And his name was Aiken Drum.

(9) And he ate up a' the baubee baps, etc.,
    And his name was Aiken Drum.

This is a Scottish rhyme. 'Aiken Drum' was a nonsense refrain to a ballad composed at the time of the battle of Sherrifmuir, during the uprising of the Jacobites in 1715. The present words were printed by James Hogg (1770—1835), one of the most notable poets in Scottish history. Can you find the drums beating in the music?

33 *The Pretty Maid*

'Where are you going to, my pret-ty maid? Where are you going to, my pret-ty maid?' 'I'm go-ing a milk-ing, sir,' she said,

'Sir,' she said, 'Sir,' she said, 'I'm go-ing a-milk-ing, sir,' she said.

(2) 'May I go with you, my pretty maid?'
    'You're kindly welcome, sir,' she said, etc.

(3) 'Say, will you marry me, my pretty maid?'
    'Yes, if you please, kind sir,' she said, etc.

(4) 'What is your father, my pretty maid?'
    'My father's a farmer, sir,' she said, etc.

(5) 'What is your fortune, my pretty maid?'
    'My face is my fortune, sir,' she said, etc.

(6) 'Then I can't marry you, my pretty maid.'
    'Nobody asked you, sir,' she said, etc.

The gracefulness of the girl this song is about is shown in the gentle, lilting rhythm. (Notice what a dot after a quaver does.) Once again you will discover what good phrasing means to musical presentation. If the phrasing is less than good the girl will not be nearly so pretty.

If you sing and play this with beautiful, smooth (legato) phrasing the music will sound as much like strawberries and cream as music can.

35 Polly Put the Kettle On

Pol - ly   put   the   ket - tle   on,   Pol - ly   put   the   ket - tle   on,

Pol - ly   put   the   ket - tle   on, We'll   all   have   tea.

Su - key take   it   off   a - gain,   Su - key take   it   off   a - gain,

Su - key   take   it   off   a - gain, They've   all   gone   a - way.

An economical left hand part. Doh, soh, high doh occupy six bars. And then there is only an imitation of a phrase in the melody. Of course it is an important phrase—the title in fact.

36 Bo-Peep

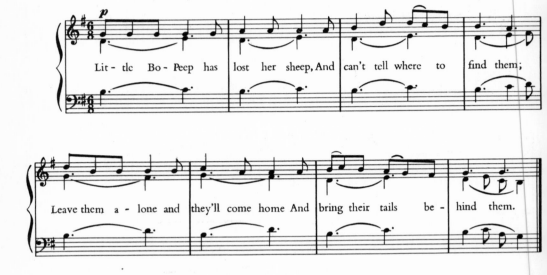

Lit-tle Bo-Peep has lost her sheep, And can't tell where to find them;
Leave them a-lone and they'll come home And bring their tails be-hind them.

(2) Little Bo-Peep fell fast asleep,
    And dreamt she heard them bleating;
    But when she awoke, she found it a joke,
    For they were still all fleeting.

(3) Then she took up her little crook,
    Determined for to find them;
    She found them indeed, but it made her heart bleed,
    For they'd left their tails behind them.

(4) It happened one day, as Bo–Peep did stray
Into a meadow hard by,
There she espied their tails side by side.
All hung on a tree to dry.

(5) She heaved a sigh, and wiped her eye,
And over the hillocks went stump-o,
And tried what she could, as a shepherdess should,
To tack again each to its rump-o.

The words of rhymes were often watered down so as to be 'suitable for children'. Those who did this didn't always know much about children. Here we have gone back to the robust year of 1810 and preferred a version which was used then.

67

37 Girls and Boys

Girls and boys come out to play! The moon doth shine as bright as day.

Leave your sup-per and leave your sleep, And join your play-fel-lows in the street.

Come with a whoop, come with a call, Come with a good will or not at all:

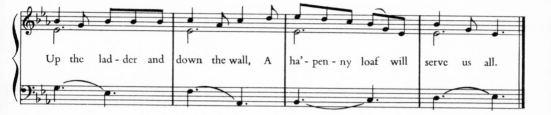

Up the lad - der and down the wall, A ha' - pen - ny loaf will serve us all.

If you have a fiddle handy you might play this melody on it. Then you will have the tune as it originally was. For it was as a dance tune printed in the eighteenth-century editions of John Playford's Dancing Master. *This was a collection which no one keen on dancing was ever without.*

38 *Bobby Shafto*

Bob-by Shaf-to's gone to sea, With sil - ver buck-les on his knee; When

he comes back he'll mar-ry me; Bon-ny Bob - by Shaf - to!

Bob - by Shaf-to's bright and fair; Comb-ing down his yel-low hair;

He's my ain for ev - er - mair; Bon-ny Bob-by Shaf-to!

Another economical accompaniment. The scale passages, the sturdy crotchets, seem to suit such a proud north-country character as was the original Robert Shafto. As he was a candidate for Parliament at one time this rhyme was useful publicity.

39 Lucy Locket and Kitty Fisher

Lu - cy Lock - et lost her pock - et, Kit - ty Fish - er found it, But

ne'er a pen - ny was there in it, But the bind - ing round it.

If the right hand part is too widely spaced for your hand leave out the lower notes on the treble stave. You will nearly always find that a melody alone with a sturdy bass will sound satisfactory. The extra middle-part notes are there because they sound attractive—as, I suppose, were Lucy and Kitty. They were celebrated for their beauty in the reign of Charles II.

The tune is also that of 'Yankee Doodle'. Whether it came from America to Britain, or the other way round, is not known. That it was published for the first time as 'Yankee Doodle' in a collection of Scotch, English, Irish and Foreign Airs by James Aird of Edinburgh in 1782 suggests that it might have originated in the United States.

40 *Turn Again Whittington*

Turn a - gain Whitt - ing - ton, Thou worth - y cit - i - zen, Lord Mayor of Lon - don.

You may turn this into a round if you wish, the second voice commencing at the third bar. The music rings all the bells that Whittington—who was Lord Mayor of London and a great benefactor of the city at the beginning of the fifteenth century—is reputed to have heard.

41 Tom, the Piper's Son

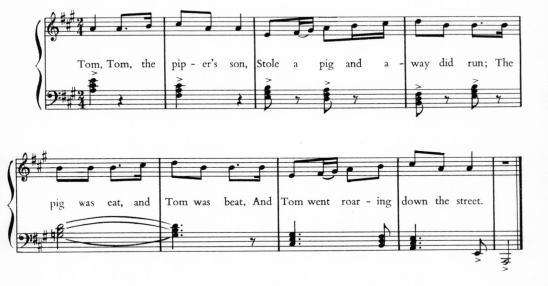

Tom, Tom, the pip - er's son, Stole a pig and a - way did run; The

pig was eat, and Tom was beat, And Tom went roar - ing down the street.

Play this as vigorously as you like, with strong accents on the grumpy chords in the left hand and the last two notes which chase Tom down the street.

42 *Jack and Jill*

Jack and Jill went up the hill To fetch a pail of wa - ter.

Jack fell down and broke his crown, And Jill came tumb - ling af - ter.

(2) Up Jack got, and home did trot,
    As fast as he could caper,
    To old Dame Dob, who patched his knob
    With vinegar and brown paper.

(3) Jill came in, and she did grin
    To see Jack's paper plaster.
    Her mother whipped her across her knee
    For laughing at Jack's disaster.

A verse which is usually left out is put back here, as an awful warning to girls not to make fun of their brothers' misfortunes. How is 'tumbling' shown in the music?

43 *Old King Cole*

Old King Cole was a mer - ry old soul, And a

mer - ry old soul was he; And he call'd for his pipe and he

call'd for his bowl, And he call'd for his fid - dlers three.

Ev'- ry fid - dler he had a fine fid - dle, A ve - ry fine fid - dle had

he, Twee - dle - dee, twee - dle - dee, went the fid- dlers three, And so

mer - ry we ___ will ___ be.

There are a lot of fifths (as from G to D) in the accompaniment. This is because the strings of fiddles are tuned in fifths (G, D, A, E,). See also p. 126. Who was the hero of this song? Some say an early British king, after whom Colchester was named; some a tradesman of Reading; others the father of the Irish chieftain Finn McCool. You can take your choice! Better really to build up your own character out of the words and music.

44 *The Duke of York*

Oh, the brave old Duke of York, He had ten thou - sand

men: He march'd them up to the top of the hill And he

marched them down a - gain. And when they were up they were

up, And when they were down they were down, And when they were on - ly

half - way up they were nei - ther up nor down.

Another military piece which gives opportunity to all who like percussion instruments (of which family the pianoforte is a sort of honorary member). Plenty of verve and a lively rhythm are required. The melody originally came from France. As in many other rhymes which refer to public figures (the Duke of York was commander-in-chief of the English army at the end of the eighteenth century) the subject was changeable. So the Duke of York stepped into balladry in the shoes of some earlier 'brave old', or 'famous', King of France.

Dr Faustus — popularly derived from the legendary figure of Faust — is a symbol of the old-time teacher who couldn't see why his pupils were not all as clever as himself. In the present setting he might have pointed out that the left hand merely repeats a theme in which all the notes of the chromatic scale occur, and that it is both logical and easy. Whether this is so is for the player to discover!

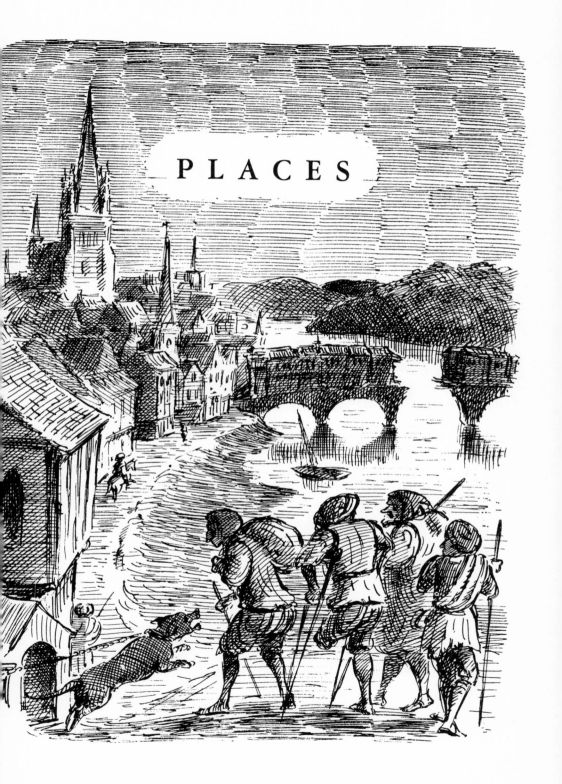

PLACES

46 Coming to Town

Hark, hark, the dogs do bark, The beg - gars are com - ing to

town: Some in rags, and some in tags, and some in vel - vet gowns.

Once upon a time beggars used to pour into the cities, and especially into London. In the music I have, however, chosen to say something about the dogs. Notice how they bark!

47 Paul's Steeple

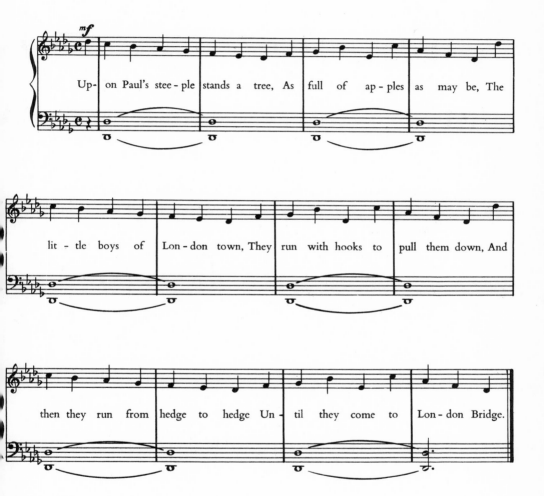

Up-on Paul's stee-ple stands a tree, As full of ap-ples as may be, The lit-tle boys of Lon-don town, They run with hooks to pull them down, And then they run from hedge to hedge Un-til they come to Lon-don Bridge.

More bells, with the biggest and deepest solemnly sounding below the chime. The steeple of old St. Paul's, the building which stood before that built by Sir Christopher Wren, fell down four hundred years ago. It was one of the sights of London and its great height stirred the imagination mightily.

48 London Bridge

(2) 'Build it up with iron bars,
    Iron bars, iron bars,
    Build it up with iron bars,
    My fair lady.'

(3) 'Iron bars will rust away', etc.

(4) 'Build it up with pins and needles', etc.

(5) 'Pins and needles rust and bend', etc.

(6) 'Build it up with penny loaves', etc.

(7) 'Penny loaves will tumble down', etc.

(8) 'Build it up with gold and silver', etc.

(9) 'Gold and silver I have not got', etc.

(10) 'Here's a prisoner I have got', etc.

(11) 'What's the prisoner done to you', etc.

(12) 'Stole my watch, and broke my chain', etc.

(13) 'What will you take to set him free', etc.

(14) 'One hundred pounds will set him free', etc.

(15) 'One hundred pounds we have not got', etc.

(16) 'Then off to prison you must go', etc.

In ancient times bridges were regarded with great veneration, for without them communication between people was difficult. So it was that bridges were honoured with all sorts of ritual. This rhyme, its character changed, carries memories of ancient and fearful sacrifices. But now it is charming, and this quality is emphasised in the arrangement of the music.

49 *The Bells of London*

(1) 'O - ran - ges   and   le - mons,' Say   the   bells   of   St.   Cle-ment's; 'You
(3) 'When ___ will   that   be?' ___ Say   the   bells   of   Step - ney; ___ 'I'm

owe   me   five   far - things,' Say   the   bells   of   St.   Mar - tin's;
sure   I   don't   know,' ___ Says   the   great   bell   of   Bow.

After 2nd time to verse 4

(2) 'When   will   you   pay   me?' Say   the   bells   of   Old   Bai - ley;

'When   I   grow   rich,'   Say   the   bells   of   Shore - ditch;

86

(4) Here comes a can - dle to light you to bed, And here comes a chop - per to chop off your head.

Perhaps, like 'London Bridge', this rhyme carries memories of long forgotten rites. These may also very well be reflected in the singing-game. The first part of the music—which gives some excellent scale practice in the left hand—is all about the bells... But in the final bars the character of the music changes. No more running quavers, but chords.

50 Over the Hills

Tom he was a pip-er's son, He learnt to play when he was young, But all the tune that he could play Was 'O-ver the hills and far a-way'. O-ver the hills and a great way off, The wind shall blow my top-knot off.

This popular eighteenth-century melody was included in the Beggar's Opera, 1728. Play the music lightly so that it seems to be going over the hills and far away. The shape of hills is drawn in the left hand melody.

51 Old Woman of Norwich

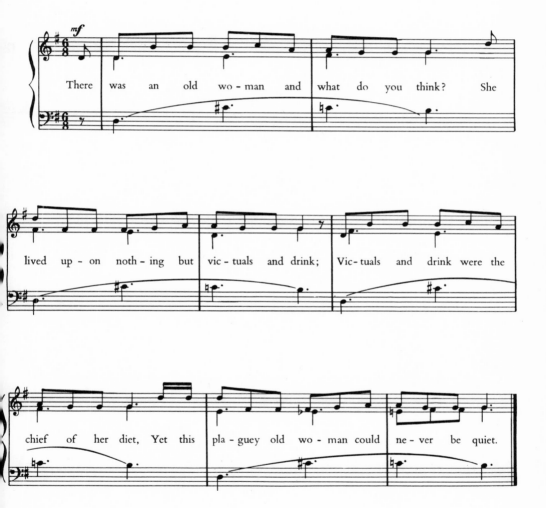

There was an old wo-man and what do you think? She
lived up-on noth-ing but vic-tuals and drink; Vic-tuals and drink were the
chief of her diet, Yet this pla-guey old wo-man could ne-ver be quiet.

There seems no reason why this old woman should belong to Norwich more than to anywhere else! She was a cross old thing wherever she came from, and that is why the chords sound rather 'plaguey'.

The Miller of Dee

There was a jol - ly mil - ler once, Lived on the ri - ver Dee;___ He

worked and sang from morn till night, No lark more blithe than he.___ And

this the bur - den of his song For e - ver used to be.... 'I

care for no - bo - dy, No, not I, If no - bo - dy cares for me.'___

(2) 'I live by my mill, God bless her! She's kindred, child, and wife;
    I would not change my station for any other in life.
    No lawyer, surgeon, or doctor, e'er had a groat from me—
    I care for nobody', etc.

(3) When spring begins its merry career, oh! how his heart grows gay;
    No summer drought alarms his fears, nor winter's sad decay;
    No foresight mars the miller's joy, who's wont to sing and say—
    'I care for nobody', etc.

(4) Thus like the miller, bold and free, let us rejoice and sing;
    The days of youth are made for glee, and time is on the wing.
    This song shall pass from me to thee, along this jovial ring—
    Let heart and voice and all agree to say 'Long live the King'.

His mill used to be by the old Dee bridge in Chester—a familiar sight to all who passed that way into Wales. In the accompaniment may be heard the sound of the mill-wheel.
'The Jolly Miller' was also introduced into Bickerstaffe's Love in a Village *in 1762.*

53 Thro' Sandgate

As I came thro' Sand - gate, thro' Sand - gate, thro' Sand - gate, As
I came thro' Sand - gate, I heard a las - sie sing: 'O
weel may the keel row, the keel row, the keel row, O
weel— may the keel row, that my— lad - die's in.'

(2) 'O who's like my Johnny,
    Sae leish, sae blithe, sae bonny?
    He's foremost among the mony
    Keel lads o' coaly Tyne.
    And weel may the keel row, etc.

(3) 'He'll set and row so tightly,
    Or in the dance, so sprightly,
    He'll cut and shuffle sightly;
    'Tis true—were he not mine.
    And weel may the keel row, etc.

(4) 'He wears a blue bonnet,
    Blue bonnet, blue bonnet;
    He wears a blue bonnet,
    A dimple in his chin.
    And weel may the keel row, etc.

This perhaps is the most famous of all traditional Northumbrian tunes. Like many others it was a dance tune (notice the snap in the rhythm) to which words were later set. The Sandgate was in Newcastle, and the keel was a flat-bottomed boat in which coal was taken to the colliers. In this arrangement we are reminded of the Northumbrian bagpipes.

54 *Coming Down to Manchester*

In com - ing down to Man - ches - ter, to gain my li - ber - ty, ___ I

saw one of the pret - tiest girls that e - ver my eyes did see; ___ I

saw one of the pret - tiest girls that e - ver my eyes did see. ___ At the

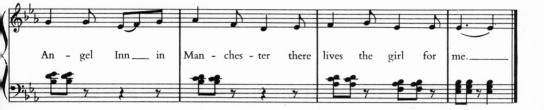

An - gel Inn___ in | Man - ches - ter there | lives the girl for | me.___

This is an interesting melody. It is very similar to that of 'The Lincolnshire Poacher'. Indeed it is 'The Lincolnshire Poacher', but is has been pulled about on its way to Lancashire. The first and the last phrase are the same, while in the middle is a second phrase which is repeated.

55 To Banbury Cross

Ride a cock-horse to Ban - bur - y Cross, To see a fine la - dy ride on a white horse; With rings on her fin - gers And bells on her toes: She shall have mu - sic wher - e - ver she goes.

Sometimes it was Coventry Cross, or Charing Cross, or Shrewsbury Cross. Sometimes it was an old woman, and sometimes a black horse. By making such variants our ancestors learned the meaning of poetry.

In the music the 'clip-clop' of the horse's hooves is to be heard every now and then. So make the two-quaver groups short and sharp (staccato).

56 Bells of Oxford

More bells in the accompaniment. But this may be sung as a round, with the voices coming in one after another at two bars' distance. This is a seventeenth-century tune. At that time rounds were very popular.

THINGS

57 Humpty Dumpty

Hump-ty Dump-ty sat on a wall, Hump-ty Dump-ty had a great fall. All the king's hors-es and all the king's men Could-n't put Hump-ty to-geth-er a-gain.

This is a riddle. Humpty Dumpty couldn't be put together again because he was an egg. But this is by no means all. In ancient times such rhymes as this contained ideas of the greatest significance. In Finnish mythology the beginning of heaven and earth was thus explained: a great egg broke, the upper half becoming heaven, the lower the earth, the yolk the sun, and the white the moon. Forms of the Humpty Dumpty rhyme are to be found in very many countries, which shows its great antiquity.

58 Hot Cross Buns

Another 'bell' tune. Compare the opening with that of 'Pussy's in the Well'. What difference do you notice? The left hand imitates the right, but the result is not quite a canon. Why not?

59 When I hae a Saxpence

When I hae a sax-pence un-der my thumb, Oh! then I get cre-dit in il - - ka toon; But when I am puir ___ they bid me go by, Oh! po - ver-ty parts ___ gude com - pan - y! Tod - dlin' hame, ___

tod - dlin' hame, As roond as a 'neep——come tod - dlin' hame.

This Scottish rhyme is taken from M. H. Mason's Nursery Rhymes and Country Songs *(1877). The melody is unusual in structure, being entirely based on the opening two bars, except for one brief interlude. Notice how it circles all the time round* doh.

60 *Christmas Pies*

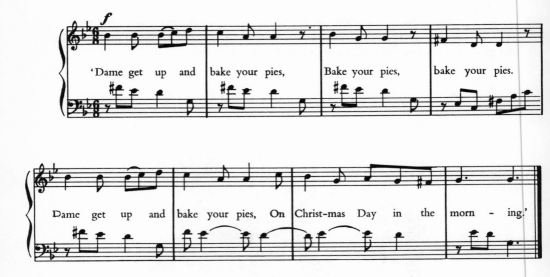

'Dame get up and bake your pies, Bake your pies, bake your pies.
Dame get up and bake your pies, On Christ-mas Day in the morn - ing,'

(2) 'Dame, what makes your maidens lie,
Maidens lie, maidens lie;
Dame, what makes your maidens lie,
On Christmas Day in the morning?'

(3) 'Dame, what makes your ducks to die,
Ducks to die, ducks to die;
Dame, what makes your ducks to die,
On Christmas Day in the morning?'

(4) 'Their wings are cut and they cannot fly,
    Cannot fly, cannot fly;
    Their wings are cut and they cannot fly,
    On Christmas Day in the morning.'

The old ladies of nursery rhymes are generally an energetic lot. See how this one bustles round early on Christmas morning. Compare both words and melody with the piece on p. 19. Here the melody is derived from 'Greensleeves'—another tune which came in handy for many different sets of words. I hope you will notice the details of the rhythm of this setting.

61 I Love Sixpence

I love six-pence, Pret-ty lit-tle six-pence, I love six-pence better than my life. I spent a pen-ny of it I lent a pen-ny of it, And I took four pence home to my wife.

(2) Oh, my little fourpence, jolly little fourpence,
    I love fourpence better than my life;
    I spent a penny of it, I lent a penny of it,
    And I took twopence home to my wife.

(3) Oh, my little twopence, jolly little twopence,
    I love twopence better than my life;
    I spent a penny of it, I lent a penny of it,
    And I took nothing home to my wife.

(4) Oh, my little nothing, jolly little nothing,
    What will nothing buy for my wife?
    I have nothing, I spend nothing,
    I love nothing better than my wife.

Some early nineteenth-century versions had twelvepence instead of sixpence. If you feel that sixpence is a too small sum to sing about these days you had better go back to twelvepence. The rhyme, however you have it, is delightful, with a touching compliment in the last line.

62 *A Song of Sixpence*

(2) The King was in his counting-house, counting out his money;
   The Queen was in her parlour, eating bread and honey,
   The maid was in the garden, hanging out her clothes,
   When up came a blackbird and pecked off her nose.

Some people say they do not like playing if there are too many sharps or flats in the key signature. If B major is difficult get used to it and then it will no longer be so. But if you want a coward's way out, play the music as though there were two flats in the signature and it will come out in B flat major. You will then need to see that every note with an accidental is—like the other notes—a semitone lower than in the key of B major. I wonder if you can see what notes have been put in to suggest the fluttering of the blackbirds?

109

63 Pat - a - Cake

'Pat - a -cake, pat - a -cake, ba - ker's man!' 'That I will, mas - ter, as

quick as I can.' 'Prick it and nick it and mark it with T, And

there will be plen - ty for ba - by and me, For ba - by and me, For

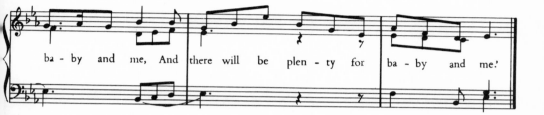

ba - by and me, And there will be plen - ty for ba - by and me.'

The baker's man was clearly kept busy; and so is the pianist. Notice the quavers in the lower part of the right hand. The same notes for a long time—because the baker's man was also doing the same thing over and over again.

64 *Scarecrow*

O all you lit - tle black-ey tops, Pray don't you eat my fa - ther's crops, While I lie down to take a nap. Shu - a ———— O! ———— Shu - a ———— O! ————

(2) If father he perchance should come,
With his cocked hat and his long gun,
Then you must fly and I must run.
Shua O! Shua O!

A charming picture of country life in olden times, when boys earned pennies by going into the fields to scare away the birds. A nice, friendly way this boy has of talking to the birds. The melodic phrase in the seventh bar was thought so highly of by whoever made up the tune that it is repeated, one note lower, in the ninth bar. This is called a sequence.

NONSENSE

65 O Dear!

O dear! What can the mat - ter be? Dear, dear! What can the mat - ter be? O dear! What can the mat - ter be? John - ny's so long at the fair. He prom - is'd to buy me a bunch of blue rib - bons, He pro - mis'd to buy me a bunch of blue rib - bons He

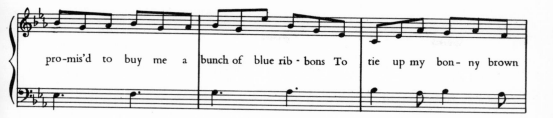

pro-mis'd to buy me a | bunch of blue rib - bons To | tie up my bon- ny brown

hair._____ And it's | O dear! | What can the mat - ter be?

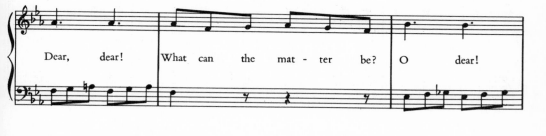

Dear, dear! | What can the mat - ter be? | O dear!

What can the mat - ter be? | John - ny's so long at the | fair.

What can the matter be? The right hand is in one key and the left hand in another.

66 See-Saw

There are a number of versions of these words. Some are more complimentary than others. But Daw used to mean the same as 'slut', and Margery was a name once common only in the poorer country districts.

This melody, noted down by M. H. Mason, is, however, quite beautiful. In the fifth bar the left hand plays a scale passage in which each note is a whole tone from its neighbour. This is known as a whole-tone scale.

67 *Paper and Ink*

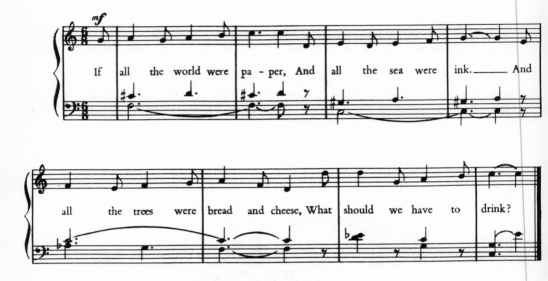

If all the world were pa-per, And all the sea were ink.___ And all the trees were bread and cheese, What should we have to drink?

(2) If all the world were sand, Oh!
Oh, then what should we lack, Oh!
If, as they say, there were no clay,
How should we take tobacco?

(3) If all our vessels ran—Ah!
If none but had a crack,
If Spanish apes ate all the grapes,
How should we do for sack?

These words date from the seventeenth century, and the melody was published in Playford's Dancing Master. Some improbable words suggest some improbable notes!

68 Hunc!

There was a lad-y loved a swine, 'Ho - ney,' said

she, 'Pig - hog, wilt thou be mine?' 'Hunc!' said he.

(2) 'I'll build thee a silver sty,
    Honey'—said she—
    'And in it thou shalt lie.'
    'Hunc!' said he.

(3) 'Pinned with a silver pin,
    Honey'—said she—
    'That thou may go out and in.'
    'Hunc!' said he.

(4) 'Wilt thou have me now,
    Honey?'—said she—
    'Speak or my heart will break.'
    'Hunc!' said he.

Notice what a wide range this melody has, from low soh *to high* doh. *I always think this a beautiful tune—a little too much so for the words; but this may be because of the way in which it is set in Roger Quilter's* Children's Overture.

69 *Robertin Tush*

Ro-bert-in Tush, he mar-ried a wife, Hop-pi-ty, hop-pi-ty, hi-ho She turned out the plague of his life, With a hi, jig, jig-gi-ty, tops and pet-ti-coat, Ro-ert-in Tush cries 'No! No!'

(2) She lay in bed till ten of the clock,
   Hoppity, etc.
   And hired a maid to put on her smock,
   With a *hi, jig*, etc.

(3) When she got up, she got up in haste,
   Hoppity, etc.
   And ran to the cupboard before she was laced,
   With a *hi, jig*, etc.

(4) She swept her house but once a year,
   Hoppity, etc.
   And that was because the brooms were dear,
   With a *hi, jig*, etc.

(5) She milked her cow but once a week,
   Hoppity, etc.
   And that was what made her butter so sweet,
   With a *hi, jig*, etc.

(6) Whenever she churned, she churned in a boot,
   Hoppity, etc.
   Instead of a staff, she used her foot,
   With a *hi, jig*, etc.

(7) She made a cheese which she laid on a shelf,
   Hoppity, etc.
   She never turned it, till it turned of itself,
   With a *hi, jig*, etc.

(8) It turned, and it turned till it came to the floor,
   Hoppity, etc.
   Then it got up and it ran to the door,
   With a *hi, jig*, etc.

(9) It rolled, and it rolled to Banbury Cross,
   Hoppity, etc.
   And she galloped after it on a white horse,
   With a *hi, jig*, etc.

Also from M. H. Mason's collection. The accompaniment picks up some of the nonsense which shows itself in the syncopations.

70 *Croodin' Doo!*

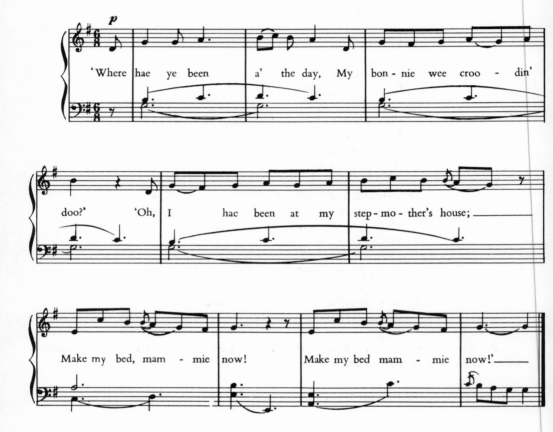

'Where hae ye been a' the day, My bon- nie wee croo- din'
doo?' 'Oh, I hae been at my step- mo- ther's house;
Make my bed, mam - mie now! Make my bed mam - mie now!'

(2) 'Where did ye get your dinner,
   My bonny wee croodin' doo?'
   'I got it in my stepmother's;
   Make my bed, mammie, now!
   Make my bed, mammie, now!'

(3) 'What did she gi'e ye to your dinner,
   My bonny wee croodin' doo?'
   'She ga'e me a little four-footed fish:
   Make my bed, mammie, now!
   Make my bed, mammie, now!'

(4) 'Where got she the four-footed fish,
   My bonnie wee croodin' doo?'
   'She got it down in yon well strand;
   O make my bed, mammie, now!
   O make my bed, mammie, now!'

(5) 'What did she do wi' the banes o't,
   My bonny wee croodin' doo?'
   'She ga'e them to the little dog;
   Make my bed, mammie, now!
   Make my bed, mammie, now!'

(6) 'O what became o' the little dog,
   My bonny wee croodin' doo?'
   'O it shot out its feet and died!
   Make my bed, mammie, now!
   Make my bed, mammie, now!'

The melody is like a lullaby. But what a sad story. A similar story exists in Scottish minstrelsy where the victim is a young nobleman—'Lord Randal'. 'Croodin' Doo!' was a favourite song of Sir Walter Scott.

71 *What are Little Boys Made Of?*

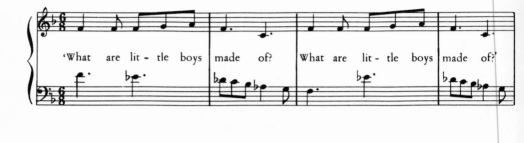

'What are lit - tle boys made of? What are lit - tle boys made of?'

'Frogs and snails and pup - py dogs' tails, And that are lit - tle boys made of.'

(2) 'What are little girls made of?
    What are little girls made of?'
    'Sugar and spice, and all that's nice,
    And that are little girls made of.'

(3) 'What are young men made of?
    What are young men made of?'
    'Sighs and leers, and crocodile tears,
    And that are young men made of.'

(4) 'What are young women made of?
    What are young women made of?'
    'Ribbons and laces, and sweet pretty faces,
    And that are young women made of.'

Here you should practise the left hand part, so that you can make all the 'wrong' notes right. Once again the left hand doesn't pay much attention to the key which the right hand is in.

72 *Cock-a-doodle Doo!*

(1) Cock - a - doo - dle doo! ___ My dame hath lost her shoe, ___ My

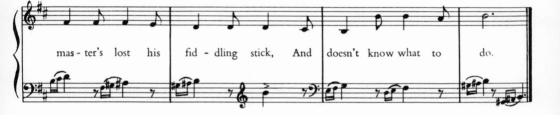

mas - ter's lost his fid - dling stick, And doesn't know what to do.

(2) Cock-a-doodle doo!
    What is my dame to do?
    Till master's found his fiddling stick
    She'll dance without her shoe.

(3) Cock-a-doodle doo!
    My dame has found her shoe,
    And master's found his fiddling stick,
    Sing cock-a-doodle doo!

*This is in an old form of minor scale. In the melody you might expect to find an A sharp;
but there isn't one. Thus the melody has a good deal of vigour. So too has the left hand part
which, as you see, crosses over the right every now and then.*

73 *Hey Diddle, Diddle*

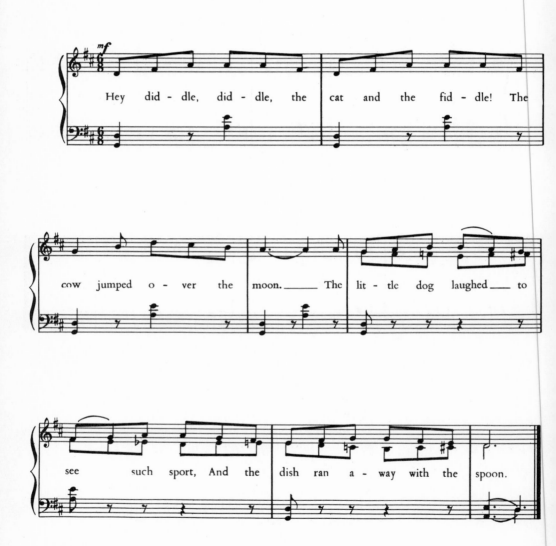

Hey did - dle, did - dle, the cat and the fid - dle! The cow jumped o - ver the moon.____ The lit - tle dog laughed ____ to see such sport, And the dish ran a - way with the spoon.

If you look back at p. 77 you will see (if you have forgotten) the tuning of the fiddle. So, now you know why the chords in the bass are as they are.

EVENING

74 *Bye, Baby Bunting*

Bye, Ba - by Bunt - ing! Dad -dy's gone a - hunt - ing. To get a lit - tle rab - bit skin To wrap a Ba - by Bunt - ing in. Bye, Ba - by Bunt - ing; Bye, Ba - by Bunt - -ing.

As you see, 6/8 time gives a natural rocking rhythm and is, therefore, frequently employed in bed-time music. Notice the use again of a pedal note (D flat in the bass). This is in the remote key of G flat major, but can easily be read as though in G major, by substituting one sharp for six flats. But I think you will agree that all the black notes in the given key improve the lullaby quality.

75 Dance to Thy Minnie

Dance to thy min - nic, My bon - ny hin - nic; Dance to thy min - nic,

My bon - ny bairn. Thou shalt have a fish - ie, In a lit - tle dish - ic,

Thou shalt have a fish - ie, When the boat comes in.

This version of an ancient singing game came from Northumberland. The idea of 'dance' is picked up by the syncopated movement of the left hand.

130

76 Hush-a-bye, Baby, Pussy's a Lady

Hush - a - bye, ba - by, puss - y's a la - dy, mous - y has gone to the mill; And if you don't cry, She'll be here by and by, So hush - a - bye, Ba - by, lie still, lie still, So hush - a -bye, Ba - by, lie still.

This is a beautiful melody. Notice the effect of the repeated doh, ray, doh *figure, of the octave leap in the third bar, and of the wide range. The chords should be spread so as to sound as far as possible like a harp.*

131

77 The Star

Twin - kle, twin - kle, lit - tle star, How I won - der what you are,

Up a - bove the world so high, Like a dia - mond in the sky;—

Twin - kle, twin - kle, lit - tle star, How I won - der what you are.

(2) When the blazing sun is gone,
    When he nothing shines upon,
    Then you show your little light,
    Twinkle, twinkle, all the night.
    Twinkle, twinkle, little star, etc.

(3) Then the traveller in the dark
    Thanks you for your tiny spark.
    Could he see which way to go
    If you did not twinkle so?
    Twinkle, twinkle, little star, etc.

(4) In the dark blue sky you keep,
    And often through my curtains peep,
    For you never shut your eye
    Till the sun is in the sky.
    Twinkle, twinkle, little star, etc.

Writing poems for children was a profitable occupation much practised by ladies at the beginning of the nineteenth century. None were more conspicuous than the sisters Jane (1783—1824) and Ann Taylor (1782—1866). 'Twinkle, twinkle, little star' was by Jane, and was first published in Rhymes for the Nursery *in 1806.*

78 Golden Slumbers

Gol - -den slum – bers kiss your eyes, Smiles — a-
wake you when you rise; Sleep pret - ty dar – ling,
do — not cry, — And I will sing a lul - la - by.

This melody was sung at the fair-grounds of London during the last part of the seventeenth century. Its popularity was such that it was included by John Gay in his Beggar's Opera. Entitled Mayfair the tune went into other operas of that period, and into the Dancing Master. The present words were added to the tune in the nineteenth century.

79 *Hush - a - Bye*

If you use both the pedals on your piano you will find that you have another musical colour, which is very suitable here. The melody is an adaptation of the seventeenth-century tune 'Lilliburlero'. If you compare the two you will see what a difference of character is brought about by the difference of speed.

80 Hush - a - ba, Babie

Hush - a - ba, ba - bie, lie still, lie still, Your mam - mie's a - wa' to the mill, — to the mill; Ba - bie is greet - ing for want of good keep - ing. Hush - a - ba, ba - bie, lie still, — lie — still.

Two points are outstanding in this melody. First, the tune centres on 'me'—frequently falling through ray to doh; second, it has a fascinating rhythm. In the fourth and fifth bars we recognise a typical rhythmic figure of Scottish music. This song was discovered in a manuscript collection in Paisley.

LIST OF WORKS CONSULTED

Mother Goose's Melody *(1791)*
The Nightingale *(c. 1800)*
Rhymes for the Nursery — *Ann and Jane Taylor (1807)*
The Thrush *(1827)*
Fifty Songs for Young People — *C. H. Purday (c. 1850)*
Popular Music of Olden Time — *William Chappell (1855–59)*
Popular Rhymes of Scotland — *Robert Chambers (1870)*
The Baby's Opera — *Walter Crane (1877)*
Nursery Rhymes and Country Songs — *M. H. Mason (1877)*
The Baby's Bouquet — *Walter Crane (1879)*
Chap-books of the Eighteenth Century — *John Ashton (1882)*
The Nursery Rhymes of England — *J. O. Halliwell (1891)*
Children's Singing Games — *Alice B. Gomme (1894)*
National Song Book — *C. V. Stanford (1905)*
Comparative Studies in Nursery Rhymes — *Lina Eckenstein (1906)*
Children's Songs of Long Ago — *A. Moffat and F. Kidson (n.d.)*
Our Old Nursery Rhymes — *A. Moffat (n.d.)*
Thirty Old Time Nursery Songs — *A. Moffat (n.d.)*
The Games of Children — *Henry Bett (1929)*
The Oxford Dictionary of Nursery Rhymes — *Iona and Peter Opie (1951)*

INDEX OF FIRST LINES